TEACHER'S RESOURCE

BLACKLINE MASTERS AND TEACHER'S GUIDE

GRADE ②

SHARE
the
Music

McGRAW-HILL

SERIES AUTHORS

Judy Bond
Coordinating Author

René Boyer-White

Margaret Campbelle-duGard

Marilyn Copeland Davidson
Coordinating Author

Robert de Frece

Mary Goetze
Coordinating Author

Doug Goodkin

Betsy M. Henderson

Michael Jothen

Carol King

Vincent P. Lawrence
Coordinating Author

Nancy L. T. Miller

Ivy Rawlins

Susan Snyder
Coordinating Author

McGraw-Hill School Division
New York   Farmington

INTRODUCTION

This **Teacher's Resource Masters** book contains supplementary activities for **Share the Music.**

The Resource Masters include the following:

- A variety of activities that reinforce or review concepts taught in the lessons. Some Resource Masters emphasize manipulative activities, while others offer written and aural activities.

- Listening maps that provide visual guidance for students as they listen to specific music selections. The listening maps help students identify melodic and rhythmic patterns, tone color, form, and other musical elements.

- Assessment questions for each unit. The assessment questions and music examples are recorded. Two recorded options are available for each question.

- Scripts for musicals.

- Tools for Assessment, including portfolio and self-assessment forms.

- An answer key.

All Resource Masters may be duplicated for classroom use. Each is keyed into the Teacher's Edition. A line at the bottom of the Resource Master identifies the page in the Teacher's Edition with which the Resource Master is intended to be used.

For listening maps, teaching suggestions are provided on the back of the Resource Master.

ACKNOWLEDGMENTS

Grateful acknowledgment is given to the following authors, composers, and publishers. Every effort has been made to trace the ownership of all copyrighted material and to secure the necessary permissions to reprint these selections. In the case of some selections for which acknowledgment is not given, extensive research has failed to locate the copyright holders.

Kaisei-sha and Scholastic, Inc. for *Tears of the Dragon* (idea/story line) by Hirosuke Hamada. Copyright © Kaisei-sha, Tokyo (Japanese). English translation by Alvin Tresselt. Reprinted by permission of Kaisei-sha and Scholastic, Inc.

Scholastic, Inc. and Kaisei-sha for *Tears of the Dragon* (idea/story line) by Hirosuke Hamada. Copyright © Kaisei-sha, Tokyo (Japanese). English translation by Alvin Tresselt. Reprinted by permission of Scholastic, Inc. and Kaisei-sha.

McGraw-Hill School Division

A Division of The **McGraw-Hill** Companies

1998 Impression

Copyright © 1995 Macmillan/McGraw-Hill School Publishing Company

All rights reserved. Permission granted to reproduce for use with Macmillan/McGraw-Hill SHARE THE MUSIC.

McGraw-Hill School Division
1221 Avenue of the Americas
New York, New York 10020

Printed in the United States of America

ISBN 0-02-295087-7 / 2

5 6 7 8 9 MAL 99 98 97

TABLE OF CONTENTS

Macmillan/McGraw-Hill

Macmillan/McGraw-Hill

Macmillan/McGraw-Hill

Macmillan/McGraw-Hill

Name _____

Say the words that rhyme. Scramble the song
strips. Put them in order.

1. Now for a song time,

Hope we sing a long time,

When we sing there's music all around !

We'll find a way now,

We can sing and play now,

Make a wonderful sound !

Macmillan/McGraw-Hill

2. Day song or night song,

Heavy song or light song,

Tunes that take us traveling away !

Dark song or bright song,

We will find the right song

For a musical day !

Macmillan/McGraw-Hill

Name_____

Make four-beat rhythm patterns.
Choose the one you like best.
Paste it on paper.

Macmillan/McGraw-Hill

RESOURCE MASTER 1•3 Practice

Writing Rhythms

Make up your own four-beat patterns. Choose
the one you like best. Paste it on paper.

Macmillan/McGraw-Hill

Writing Notes

1. Draw a note around each line.

2. Draw a note in each space.

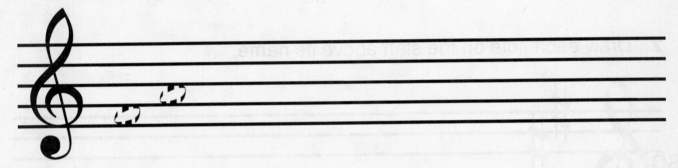

3. Cut and paste the notes below on the staff.

Macmillan/McGraw-Hill

RESOURCE MASTER 1•5 Practice

Mi So La

1. Look carefully at these notes.

mi   so   la

2. Draw each note on the staff above its name.

so   mi   la

3. Write your own melody using *mi so la*.

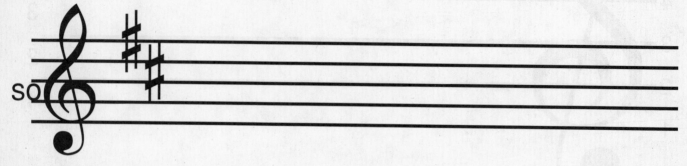

(See answers at the back of this book.)

Macmillan/McGraw-Hill

Name _____

Taking a Walk

1.

What did you see on your walk?

2. Write your answer on the staff.

3. Draw a picture of what you saw on your walk.

Macmillan/McGraw-Hill

RESOURCE MASTER 1•7 Assessment

Check It Out

1. How would you move to this music?
   a. With a steady beat.
   b. With no steady beat.

2. Which rhythm do you hear?

3. Choose the pitches you hear.

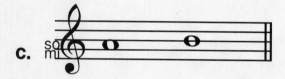

4. Which melody do you hear?

(See answers at the back of this book.)

Macmillan/McGraw-Hill

Name _____

Circle places between words when you hear a
rest. Listen for a surprise.

Toaster Time
by Eve Merriam

Tick   tick   tick   tick   tick   tick   tick

Toast   up   a   sandwich   quick   quick   quick

Hamwich

Or   jamwich

Lick   lick   lick!

Tick   tick   tick   tick   tick   tick–stop!

POP!

From THERE IS NO RHYME FOR SILVER by Eve Merriam.
Copyright © 1962, 1990 by Eve Merriam.
Reprinted by permission of Marian Reiner for the author.

Macmillan/McGraw-Hill

Name_____

RESOURCE MASTER 2•2 Practice

Writing Rhythms

Macmillan/McGraw-Hill

Name _____

Arrange the squares in the boxes on page 10.
Leave some boxes blank. Clap and say your
pattern. Glue the pictures in place.

Macmillan/McGraw-Hill

RESOURCE MASTER 2•3 Pattern

Reading Rhythms

Arrange the rhythm cards in patterns. Clap and say the pattern.

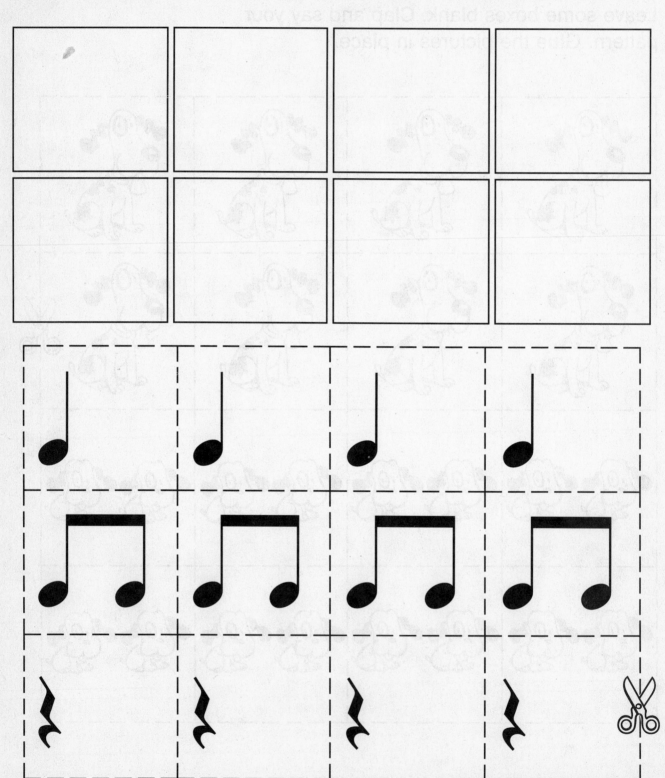

Macmillan/McGraw-Hill

Writing *So Mi Do*

Sing "Mother, Mother."
Fill in the missing pitch names. Then fill in the notes.

1.

so   mi   so   mi

2.

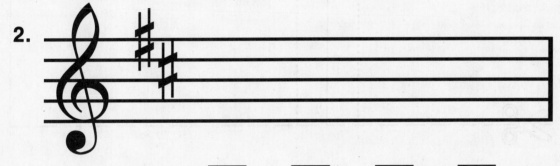

3.

4.

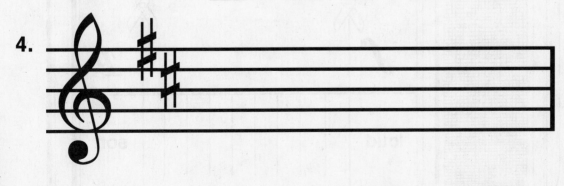

Macmillan/McGraw-Hill

(See answers at the back of this book.)

RESOURCE MASTER 2•5 Practice

Loud and Soft

Cut out the marker and fold in half along the solid line. Then fold along the dotted lines to look line this: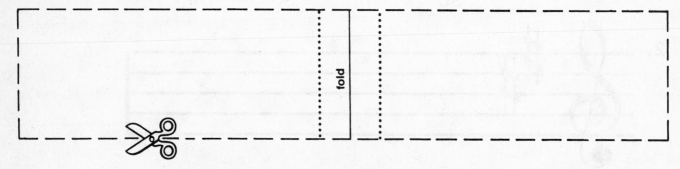
Cut slits into the radio. Put each end of your marker through a slit. As you listen to the music, move your marker to f when the music is loud. Move it to p when the music is soft.

fold

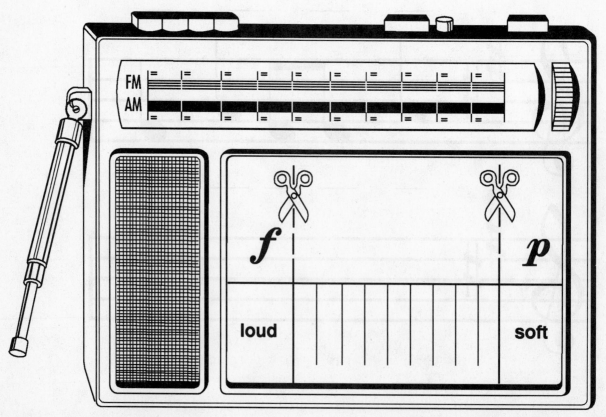

f   p

loud   soft

Macmillan/McGraw-Hill

Name _____

"If You Need a Buddy"

Write "f" or "p" in the boxes. Perform "If You Need a Buddy" for the class.

If You Need a Buddy

Words and Music by Sue Snyder

1. If you need a bud-dy,   whis-tle.   *(whistle)*

If you need a pal, just   let   me   know, 'Cause

I will be your bud-dy,   I will be your pal.

Friends wher - ev - er we   go.

Macmillan/McGraw-Hill

A Rhythm Game

Make up different eight-beat patterns with your cards. Clap or say the rhythms.

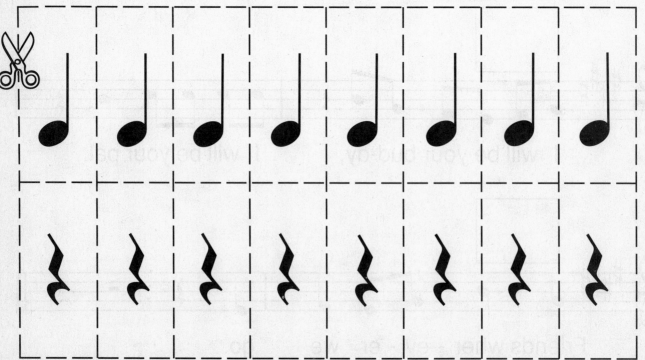

Macmillan/McGraw-Hill

Check It Out

1. On which beat do you hear a rest?

2. What do you hear?

a.

b.

c.

3. Choose the rhythm you hear.

4. Which melody do you hear?

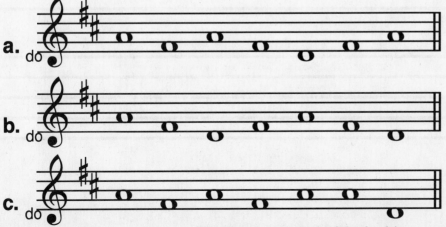

(See answers at the back of this book.)

Name _____

Overture from *The Nutcracker*

by Piotr Ilyich Tchaikovsky

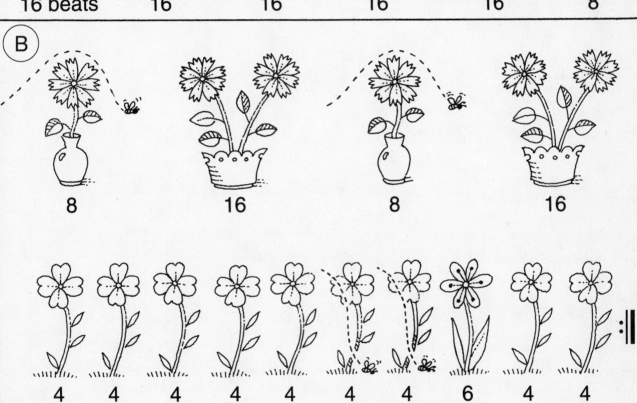

Coda

4

Macmillan/McGraw-Hill

USING RESOURCE MASTER 2•9

DIRECTIONS:

Distribute a copy of the Resource Master to each child. Point out the large sections labeled A and B, then the Coda. Explain that each picture represents a small part of the larger sections labeled A or B, or the coda. The number of beats is given to help keep track of elapsed time (the number of petals on each flower corresponds to the number of beats for that flower). Tell children that similar pictures indicate that the music will sound the same in those parts. You may wish to have children find same and different pictures before listening. Be sure to mention and explain the repeat sign before listening. You may wish to create movements to be performed by children with this recording, one type of movement for each section.

Name _____

March from *The Nutcracker*
by Piotr Ilyich Tchaikovsky

1 symbol
= 1 measure of $\frac{4}{\quad}$

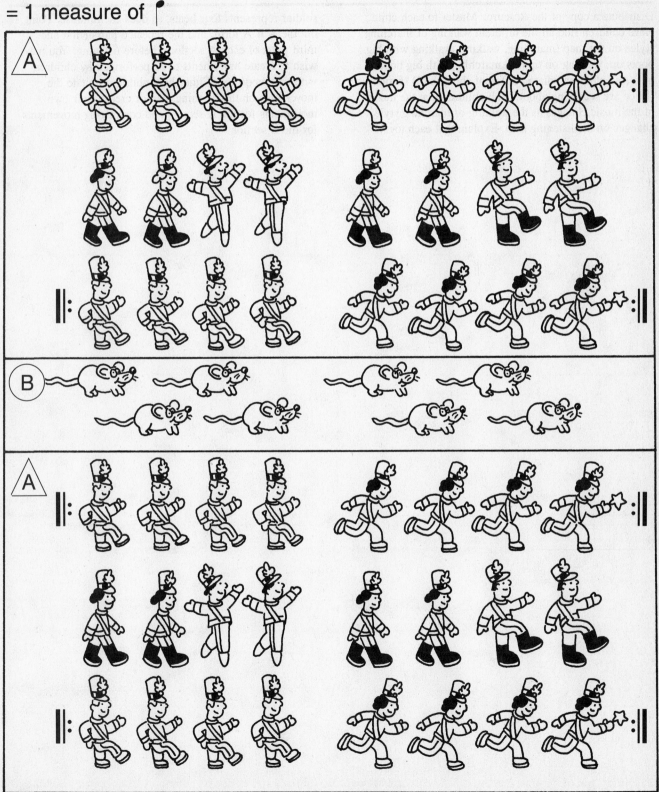

Macmillan/McGraw-Hill

21

USING RESOURCE MASTER 2·10

DIRECTIONS:

Distribute a copy of the Resource Master to each child. Have children find all the different walking or marching styles on the map (marching, walking, walking with big boots on, walking on tiptoes, marching with big boots on). Ask children what is different about the B section. (Mice are scurrying about.) Tell children that the mood of the music changes as the walking or marching style changes on the listening map. Explain that each toy soldier represents four beats, as does each mouse. Point out the A B A form, and the repeated parts (first and third parts of each A section), before listening. You may wish to create movements to be performed by children with this recording. Either have children imitate the movements on the listening map or create their own movements for the A section and contrasting movements for the B section.

Name _____

Dance of the Sugar Plum Fairy
from *The Nutcracker*
by Piotr Ilyich Tchaikovsky

1 symbol = 1 measure of $\frac{4}{4}$

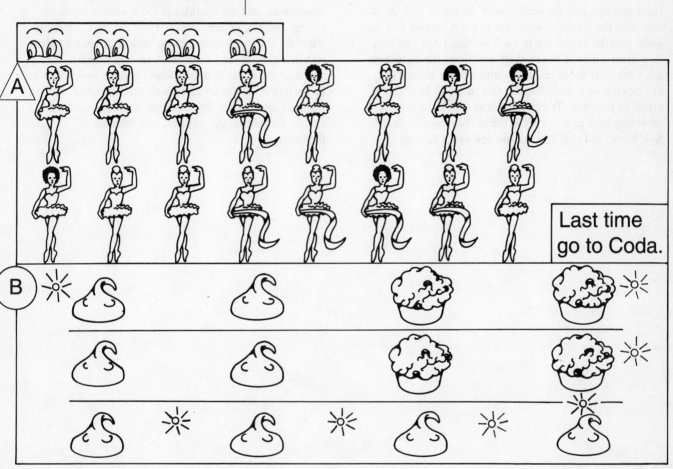

Last time go to Coda.

Interlude

Go back to Ⓐ

Macmillan/McGraw-Hill

DIRECTIONS:

Distribute a copy of the Resource Master to each child. Have children find the section with the fairies and the section with the sweets. (Fairies are in the A section and the coda, and the sweets are in the B section.) Ask children how many kinds of sweets there are. (two) Have children tell what is different about the fairies in the coda. (They are moving very fast.) Explain that they will hear faster music in the coda. Tell children that each large symbol, including each pair of eyes in the introduction, lasts for four beats. Tell children that the downward flowing scarves in the A section represent descending scales in the woodwinds, and the sparkles in the B section represent sudden, higher, louder sounds. Point out the contrasting interlude and the direction to go back to A after it. Mention that after the last time the A section is heard, they will hear the coda. You may wish to create movements to be performed by the children with this recording. Divide the class into four groups and create movements for the fairies, the sweets, the muffins, and the stars of the interlude.

Chinese Dance from *The Nutcracker*
by Piotr Ilyich Tchaikovsky

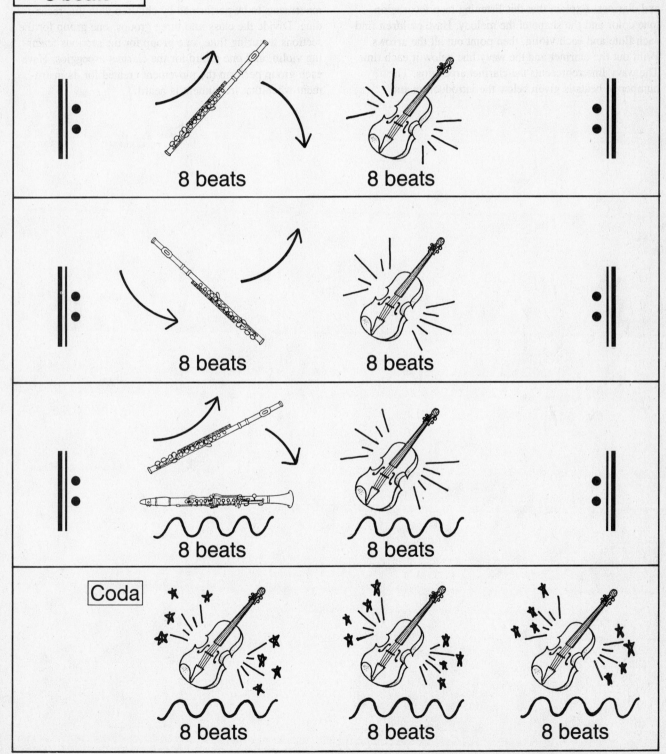

Introduction 8 beats

8 beats   8 beats

8 beats   8 beats

8 beats   8 beats

Coda

8 beats   8 beats   8 beats

Macmillan/McGraw-Hill

USING RESOURCE MASTER 2•12

DIRECTIONS:

Distribute a copy of the Resource Master to each child. Have children tell what they know about the flute, violin, and clarinet. Explain that this listening map focuses on tone color and the shape of the melody. Have children find each flute and each violin, then point out all the arrows. Point out the clarinet and the wavy line below it each time. The wavy line represents the clarinet arpeggios. The number of beats is given below the introduction and each instrument to show elapsed time. Be sure to note the repeat signs before listening. You may wish to create movements to be performed by children with this recording. Divide the class into three groups, one group for the sections featuring flute, one group for the sections featuring violin, and one group for the clarinet arpeggios. Have each group perform the movement created for its instrument when that instrument is heard.

Name _____

Waltz of the Flowers (excerpt)
from *The Nutcracker*
by Piotr Ilyich Tchaikovsky

KEY	1 flower = 3 beats

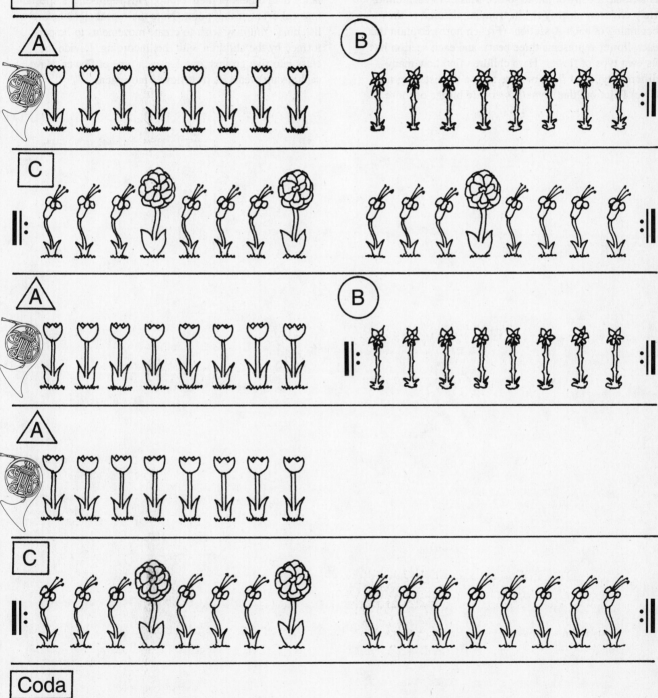

Macmillan/McGraw-Hill

USING RESOURCE MASTER 2•13

DIRECTIONS:

Distribute a copy of the Resource Master to each child. Help children identify the instrument pictured at the beginning of each A section. (French horn) Explain that each flower represents three beats, and each section has its own type of flower. Have children find how many different types of flowers there are on the listening map. (five) Point out that some flowers are bigger or more fancy than others in their group. This represents a special musical event at that point. Note the repeat signs before listening. You may wish to create movements to be performed by the children with this recording. Divide the class into five groups, one for each type of flower. Have each group create its own flower movement.

Trace these pathways.

Finish the pathways.

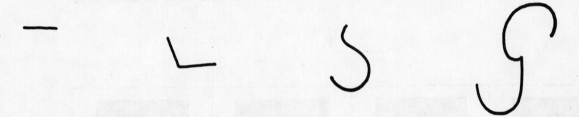

Now draw some pathways of your own.

Try out a pathway in the air or on the floor.

Macmillan/McGraw-Hill

RESOURCE MASTER 3•2 Practice

Rhythm Patterns

Show the rhythm pattern of
"Here Comes a Bluebird."

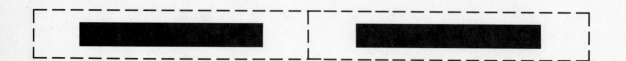

(See answers at the back of this book.)

Macmillan/McGraw-Hill

Macmillan/McGraw-Hill

Name_____

Dove Stick Puppets

Paste the doves to craft sticks. As you listen
to the music, show the forte or piano sign to
match what you hear.

Name_____

Writing Half Notes

1. These notes show a sound that lasts for two beats.

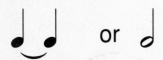

2. Circle the half notes.

3. Write some half notes.

Macmillan/McGraw-Hill

4/4 Rhythms

Make flash cards to show rhythms in 4/4
Clap your rhythms.

Macmillan/McGraw-Hill

Instrument Families

Woods

Metals

Drums

Scrapers/Shakers

Macmillan/McGraw-Hill

Paste the squares on the correct shelves.

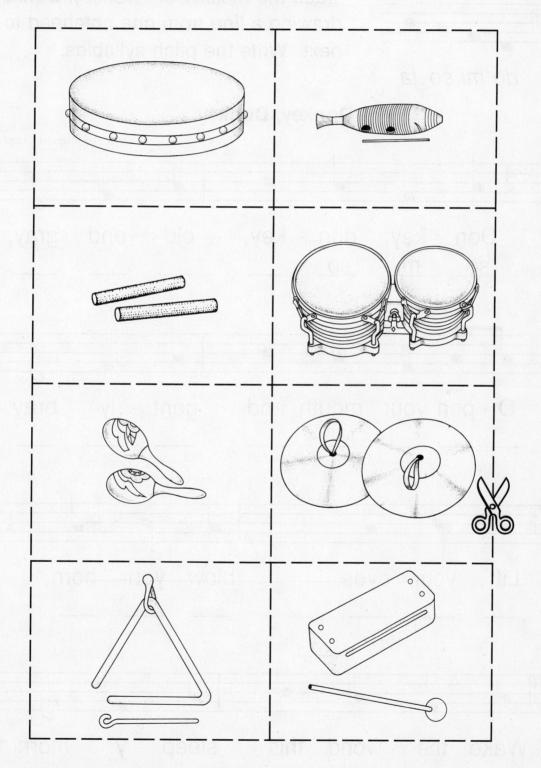

Macmillan/McGraw-Hill

RESOURCE MASTER 3•7 Practice

Melodic Shape

do mi so la

Trace the melody of "Donkey, Donkey" by drawing a line from one notehead to the next. Write the pitch syllables.

Donkey, Donkey

Old English Rhyme
Music by Margaret Campbelle-duGard

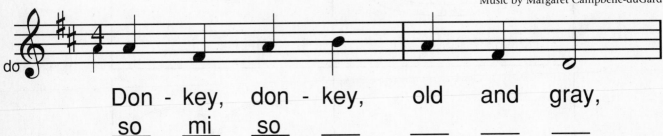

do

Don - key,   don - key,   old   and   gray,
so   mi   so   ___   ___   ___

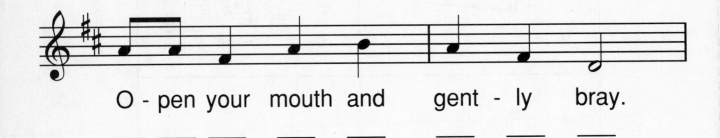

O - pen   your   mouth   and   gent - ly   bray.
___   ___   ___   ___   ___   ___   ___

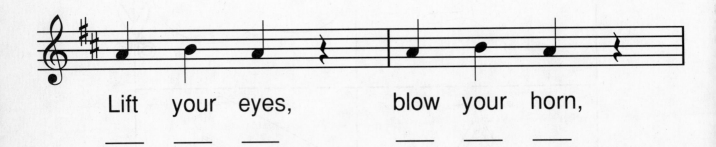

Lift   your   eyes,   blow   your   horn,
___   ___   ___   ___   ___   ___

Wake   the   world   this   sleep - y   morn.
___   ___   ___   ___   ___   ___   ___

(See answers at the back of this book.)

Macmillan/McGraw-Hill

Name _____

Check It Out

1. Which instrument family do you hear?

a. drums   **b.** metals   **c.** woods   **d.** scrapers/shakers

2. Choose the rhythm you hear.

3. Which rhythm do you hear?

4. Which order do you hear?

a. woods   metals   drums   scrapers/shakers

b. metals   woods   drums   scrapers/shakers

c. scrapers/shakers   drums   metals   woods

(See the back of this book for answers.)

Macmillan/McGraw-Hill

RESOURCE MASTER 3•9 SCRIPT

Romper, Stomper, and Boo

Once there were three elephants
who were the best of friends.
Their names were Romper,
Stomper, and Boo. They each
got their name by the way
they went down the path in
the jungle.

Romper was always in a hurry. Stomper was not in
such a big hurry, but he made SO MUCH NOISE!
Boo was a most unusual elephant. Boo walked down
the path with slow, quiet, careful steps, not even
cracking a twig, and would come right up behind
you before you knew it and say "BOO!"

One day the three elephants were talking
under their favorite tree, when all of a
sudden there was a big commotion in
the trees. The birds squawked, "What
could be the problem?" [Say three
times.] Then the monkeys chattered,
"Um, um, terrible, terrible!" [Say
three times.]

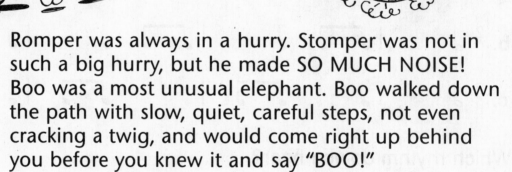

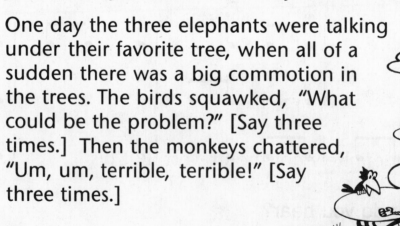

Use with page 125. • Grade 2

Macmillan/McGraw-Hill

The problem was that the trappers had arrived in the jungle to trap animals—and they were especially interested in ELEPHANTS!

The three elephants decided what to do. Romper was the oldest, so he set out to scare the trappers away. But he made so much noise ROMP ROMP ROMPING as he hurried down the path that the trappers heard the sound a mile away. They had a net ready for Romper and a cage!

When Romper did not come back, there was an awful commotion in the trees. (Birds and monkeys repeat their words.)

Stomper and Boo decided what to do. Stomper was the next oldest, so she set out to scare the trappers away. But she made so much noise STOMP STOMP STOMPING down the path that the trappers heard the sound two miles away. They had a net ready for Stomper and a cage!

When Stomper did not come back, there was an awful commotion in the trees. (Birds and monkeys repeat their words.)

Little Boo was the only one left. He was the youngest and definitely not the bravest. But his friends were in trouble, so Boo set off down the jungle pathway in his usual quiet Boo way.

Macmillan/McGraw-Hill

Boo walked quietly into the camp while the trappers were taking their afternoon naps. He unlatched the cages and the three elephants quietly sneaked out of the camp. They walked all the way through the jungle the way Boo walked—slowly, carefully, quietly, until they were safely underneath their favorite tree.

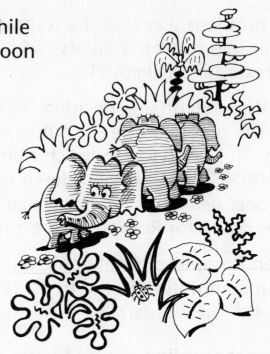

When the trappers awakened, the cages were empty. They cried, "How did those elephants get away? We didn't hear a sound! They are much too clever for us!" And the trappers quickly folded up their tents and left the jungle, never to return.

The birds began to sing, "The trappers are gone." [Say three times.] The monkeys began to chatter, "Um, um, wonderful, wonderful." [Say three times.] And Boo was the hero of that day!

Macmillan/McGraw-Hill

Dance a Minuet!

Make up a minuet.

1. Face your partner or stand side by side.

2. Move backward, forward, or side to side.

Backward   Forward   Side to Side

3. You can move on just the first beat, or on beats one, two, and three.

4. Choose other moves to include in your dance.

Macmillan/McGraw-Hill

RESOURCE MASTER 4•2 Practice

Find the Notes: *do mi so la*

Write in the pitch names.
Which lines of music are the same?

Macmillan/McGraw-Hill

As you listen to "Hop, Old Squirrel", make the
squirrel hop on the correct log for each pitch.

See answers at the back of this book.

Macmillan/McGraw-Hill

do re mi with Acorns

Work in groups of three. Choose an acorn. If you choose *mi*, sit on a chair. If you choose *re*, kneel on the floor. If you choose *do*, sit on the floor. When your teacher says "Scramble", exchange cards.

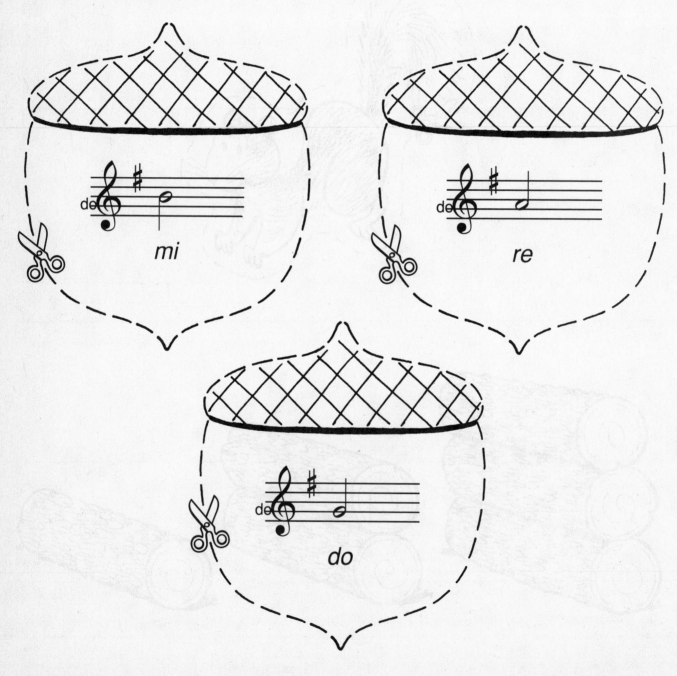

Macmillan/McGraw-Hill

Name _____

Identify Pitches *do re mi so*

Fill in the missing pitches.

do   re   mi   do   so   mi   so   do

Fill in the missing pitch names.

do

___ ___ ___ ___ ___ ___ ___ ___

Macmillan/McGraw-Hill

See answers at the back of this book.

Cut out the notes. Create your own melody.

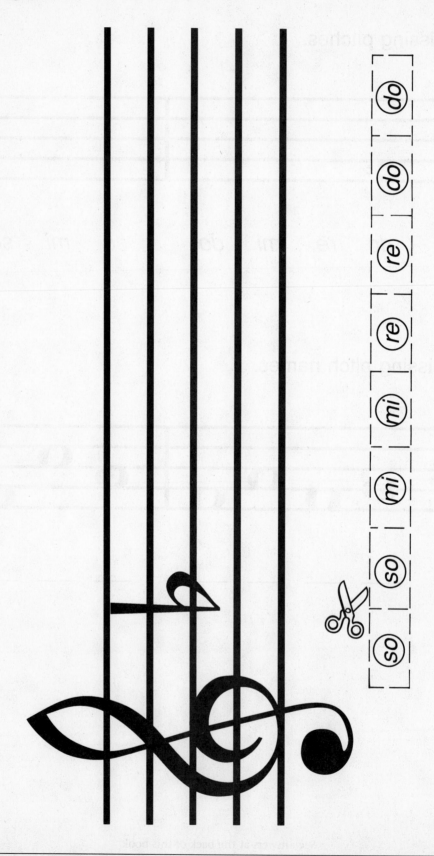

Macmillan/McGraw-Hill

Name _____

Writing Rhythms in ¾

Use ♩ ♫ ♪ 𝄽 ♩ ♩. to write groups of
3 beat rhythms.

Choose four measures to make a pattern.
Clap the pattern for your class.

Macmillan/McGraw-Hill

RESOURCE MASTER 4•7 Practice

"Sasara Ang Bulaklak"

Write the missing pitch syllables.

Tagalog: Sa - sa - ra ang bu - lak - lak,

bu - bu - ka ang bu - lak - lak,

I - i - kot ang bu - lak - lak,

Da - da - an ang rey - na.

Sing the words of the next section.

Bum ti-ya ya, bum ti-ya ya
bum ti-ya ya ye - ye

Bum ti-ya ya, bum ti-ya ya,
bum ti-ya ya ye - ye a bom!

See answers at the back of this book.

Use with page 150. • Grade 2

Macmillan/McGraw-Hill

Name _____

Make a Melody

Write the pitches you choose. Clap the
rhythm of each line.

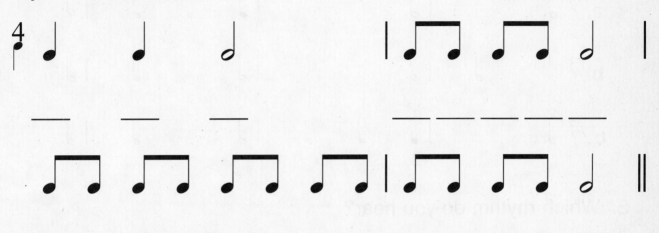

Write your melody.

Then perform it.

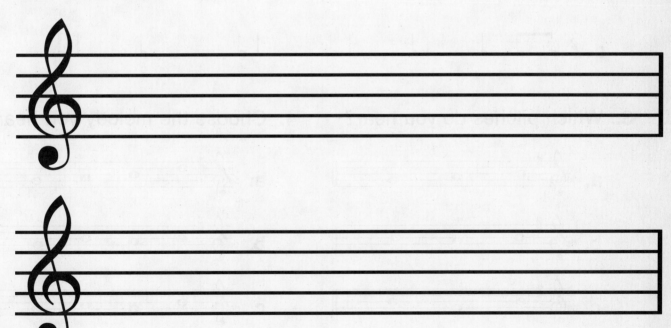

Macmillan/McGraw-Hill

Check It Out

1. Choose the rhythm you hear.

  a.

  b.

  c.

2. Which rhythm do you hear?

  a.

  b.

  c.

3. Which pitches do you hear?

  a.

  b.

  c.

4. Choose the melody you hear.

  a.

  b.

  c.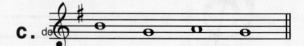

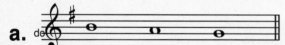

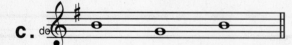
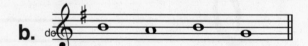

Macmillan/McGraw-Hill

Name _____

Horns Around the World

Make a book about different horns around the world. Color the pictures. Share your book with others.

HORNS AROUND

THE WORLD

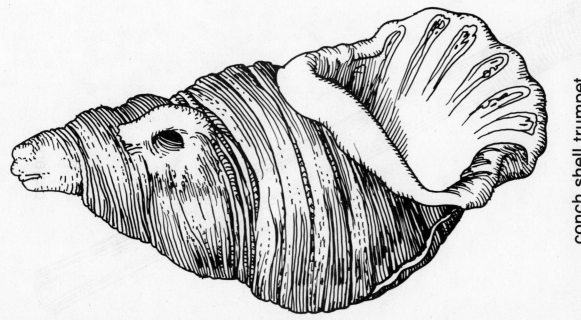

conch shell trumpet

Macmillan/McGraw-Hill

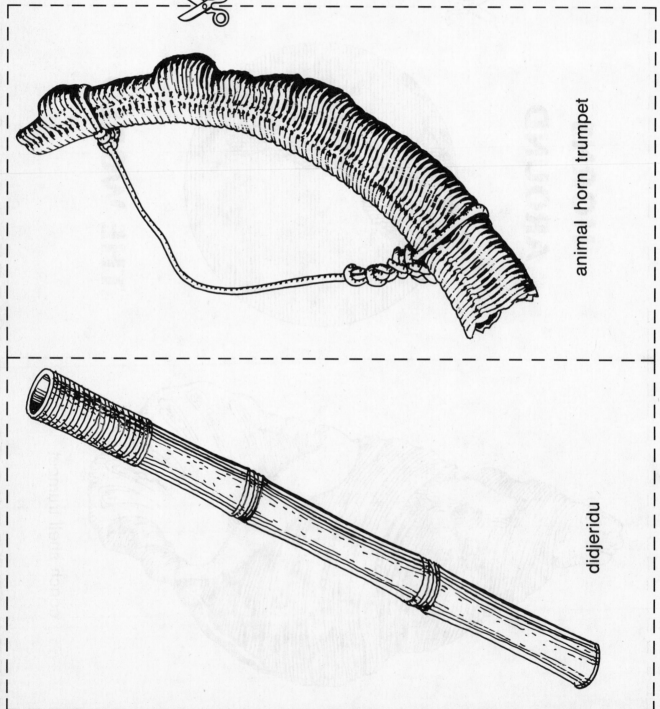

animal horn trumpet

didjeridu

Macmillan/McGraw-Hill

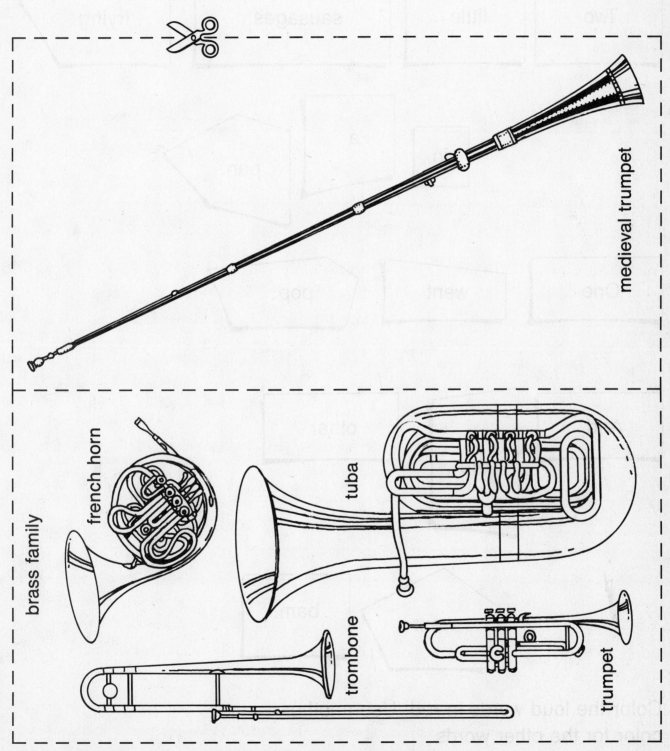

medieval trumpet

brass family

french horn

tuba

trombone

trumpet

"Two Little Sausages"

Two little sausages frying

in a pan.

One went pop.

And the other

went bam.

Color the loud words in red. Use another color for the other words.

Macmillan/McGraw-Hill

Name _____

"Bill Grogan's Goat"

Color the echo parts of the song.

American Folk Song

There was a man (there was a man)

Now, please take note, (now, please take note)

There was a man (there was a man)

Who had a goat. (who had a goat)

He loved that goat, (he loved that goat)

In - deed he did, (in - deed he did)

He loved that goat (he loved that goat)

Just like a kid. (just like a kid)

Macmillan/McGraw-Hill

Name_____

Where's the Brass?

Look closely at this picture. Can you find the instruments in it? Trace and then color the instruments.

See answers at the back of this book.

Macmillan/McGraw-Hill

Name _____

Check It Out

1. Listen to a pattern with an accented sound.
Circle the symbol that needs to be added
to show that the sound is suddenly louder.

a. ♩   **b.** ——◁   **c.** ⫶‖   **d.** >

2. Circle the beat in this rhythm where you
hear an accent.

3. How would you move to this music?

a. trot

b. gallop

4. What do you hear?

a. music with equal sounds

b. music with unequal sounds

Macmillan/McGraw-Hill

See answers at the back of this book.

RESOURCE MASTER 5•5 Pattern

Paper Weaving

Weave a paper placemat.

1. You will need two sheets of paper. Choose different colors.

2. Make warp strips by cutting one sheet of paper. Leave 1″ uncut at the top and sides of each strip.

3. Make weft strips by cutting strips out of the second sheet of paper.

4. Weave the weft strips through the warp strips, over and under. The next strip will go under and over.

Macmillan/McGraw-Hill

Name _____

Make Your Own Rhythms
Page 1

a.

b.

c.

d.

1. Which pattern says "tapping 𝄾 tapping 𝄾 "? _____

2. Which pattern says "knocking at the front
   door"? _____

3. Which pattern says "who's that singing 𝄾 "? _____

4. Which pattern says "I - hear you"? _____

See answers at the back of this book.

Macmillan/McGraw-Hill

RESOURCE MASTER 6•1 Practice

Page 2

Put four measures together. Perform your
rhythms for the class.

Macmillan/McGraw-Hill

Name _____

Rhythmic Building Blocks

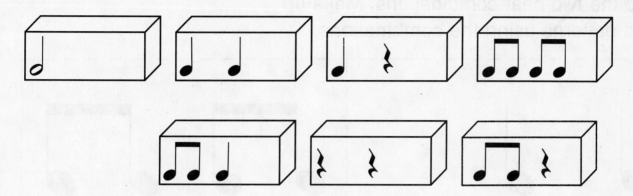

1. Write two beat rhythms to fill each measure.

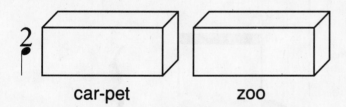

car-pet   zoo

2. Think of two ways to write these word patterns.

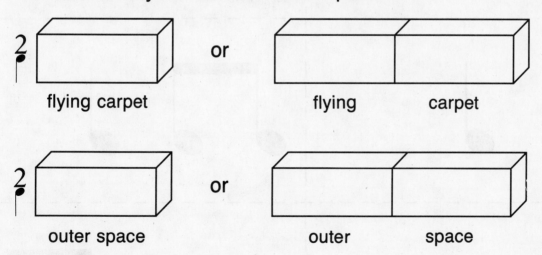

flying carpet   or   flying   carpet

outer space   or   outer   space

3. Make your own patterns using the symbols
you know.

See answers at the back of this book.

Macmillan/McGraw-Hill

RESOURCE MASTER 6•3 Practice

Rhythm Flash Cards

Clap the two-beat combinations. Make up
word patterns using the combinations.

Macmillan/McGraw-Hill

Name _____

Color and cut out the shapes below. Then use
them to show the form of the music you hear.

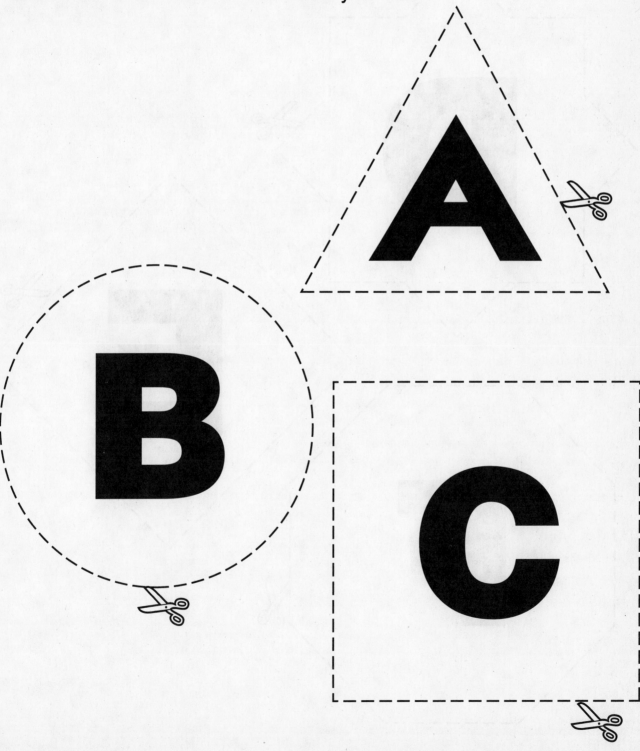

Macmillan/McGraw-Hill

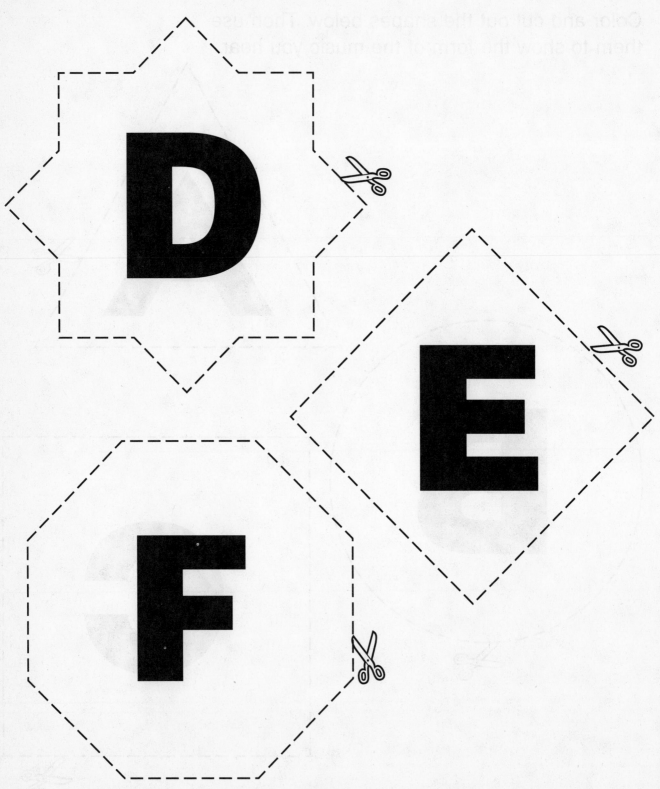

Macmillan/McGraw-Hill

Name

Pitch Stairs

Point to each stair to match each pitch you sing.

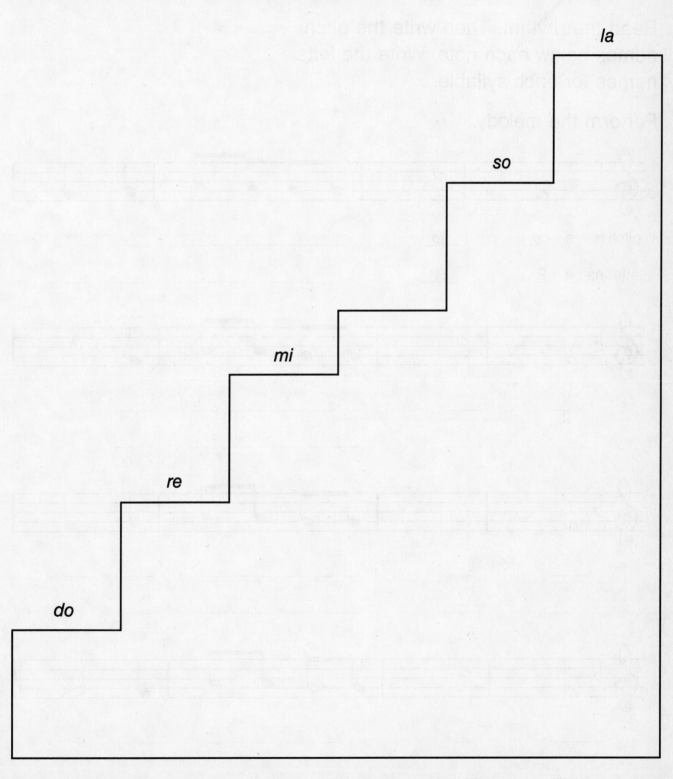

Macmillan/McGraw-Hill

The Mystery Melody

Can you guess the name of this melody?

Read the rhythm. Then write the pitch
names below each note. Write the letter
names for each syllable.

Perform the melody.

Macmillan/McGraw-Hill

Name_____

RESOURCE MASTER 6•7 Assessment

Check It Out

1. Which form do you hear?

   a. AA   **b.** AB   **c.** rondo form   **d.** ABA

2. Which rhythm pattern do you hear?

3. Choose the rhythm you hear.

4. Choose the form you hear.

   a. AB   **b.** ABA   **c.** rondo   **d.** something else

See answers at the back of this book.

Use with page 248. • Grade 2   **67**

Macmillan/McGraw-Hill

Find the Rhymes

Circle the words that rhyme. Connect the words
with lines.

America

My country, 'tis of thee,

Sweet land of liberty,

Of thee I sing;

Land where my fathers died,

Land of the Pilgrim's pride,

From ev'ry mountainside

Let freedom ring.

Macmillan/McGraw-Hill

In the Hall of the Mountain King
from *Peer Gynt Suite* No. 1
by Edvard Grieg

USING RESOURCE MASTER C·2

DIRECTIONS:

Distribute a copy of the Resource Master to each child. Echo-clap the rhythm of the theme with the children, first in 2-measure units, then all together. Have them clap the rhythm at slow and fast tempos. Have the children look at the map before listening, and ask them what they notice about the way the boy is moving along the path. (He starts out slowly and goes faster and faster.) Ask the children what they notice about the path. (It is small at the beginning and gets wider from left to right, like a crescendo marking, meaning "to get louder.") Notice the numbers. Each number stands for one occurrence of the theme. Number 19 is the coda, the fastest part of the selection.

A Thanksgiving Poem

After reading the poem "Thanksgiving,"
write two more verses.
Finish the following sentences:

Thank you for all my nose can smell—

_____

_____

_____

Thank you for all my mouth can taste—

_____

_____

_____

Read the poem again to the class. Include
your verses.

Macmillan/McGraw-Hill

RESOURCE MASTER C•4 Story

Bert's Thanksgiving

Follow along as you listen to the story.

Bert was a turkey who liked to dance. One day,
he saw a group of dancers performing for the
King and the Queen as they were out on their daily
promenade about the grounds. He saw how they
enjoyed the dance and it gave him an idea. He
managed to get an appointment with the King and
the Queen and danced before them. (Perform "A
Turkey Named Bert.") They liked the dance and
decided that Bert could live in the palace. So he
became a royal turkey.

One day, Bert overheard the cooks talking.
Thanksgiving was coming soon and it was time
to choose the turkeys to serve. Bert, thinking of his
fellow turkeys, felt guilty since he was living in the
security of the palace. He sneaked out at night and
warned the first five turkeys he met that the cook
was coming. They fled up into a tree. Though the
cook looked and looked, he couldn't find them
anywhere.

Use with page 263. • Grade 2

Macmillan/McGraw-Hill

The next morning, a family was riding through the woods in a sleigh when one of the children shouted: "Stop! Look up in that tree!" The youngest child got out of the sleigh, amazed to see five turkeys in one tree! "Who are you and why are you in a tree?" she asked. The turkeys replied:

> Five fat turkeys are we,
> We slept all night in a tree.
> When the cook came around
> We couldn't be found,
> So that's why we're here, you see.

"Who are you and where are you going?" the turkeys asked.

"We're going to Grandmother's house. She lives just over the river and through the woods." (Sing "Over the River and Through the Wood.") The turkeys said, "Why don't you stop by and take Bert with you. He's the one who saved us." When the family arrived, the house was filled with the smells of good things to eat—sweet potatoes, cranberry sauce, brussels sprouts, and pumpkin pie. Bert was there as the guest of honor, instead of the main course!

The Sleigh Ride from *Musical Sleigh Ride*
by Leopold Mozart

KEY	⊃ = 2 beats p	⊃ = 2 beats f

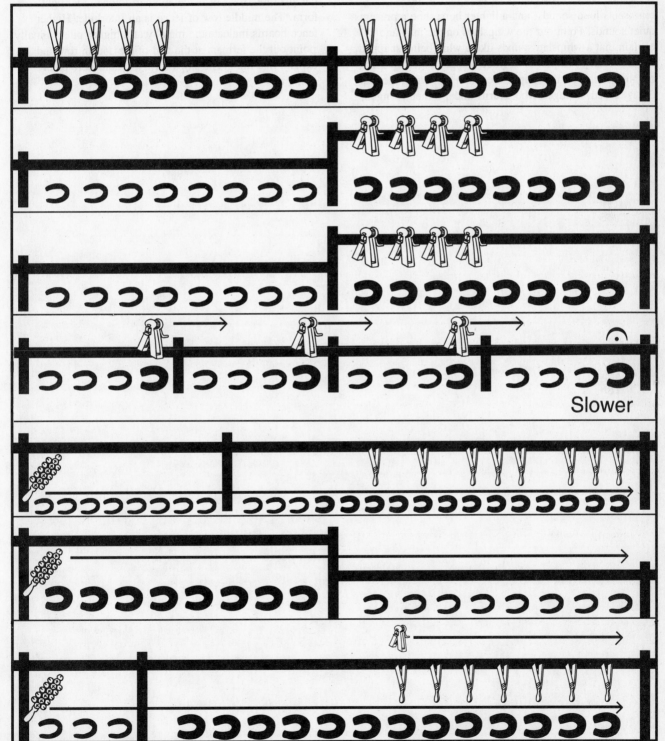

Slower

Macmillan/McGraw-Hill

DIRECTIONS:

Distribute a copy of the Resource Master to each child. Point out the key to the children and explain that one horseshoe lasts for two beats. A heavy horseshoe represents loud sounds, and a lighter horseshoe represents quiet sounds. Point out the whipslaps on the map and explain that a whipslap sounds like a whip being snapped, but it is really two pieces of wood slapped together. Point out the rachets on the map and explain that when the handle is turned, a ridged wheel turns under a metal tongue, causing a loud sound. Point out the jingle bells. Have children color the first three rows of fence one color and the last three rows of fence another color to highlight A B form. The middle row of fence is an interlude. Higher fence boards indicate the melody at a higher pitch. Finally, point out the fermata at the end of the fourth row and explain that the music stops for a moment here before going on.

A Hummingbird

Color and cut out the hummingbird. As you
listen to "A Hummingbird," move your bird up
when the sounds you hear are high. Move the
bird down when the sounds you hear are low.

Macmillan/McGraw-Hill

Holi Song
Indian Folk Music

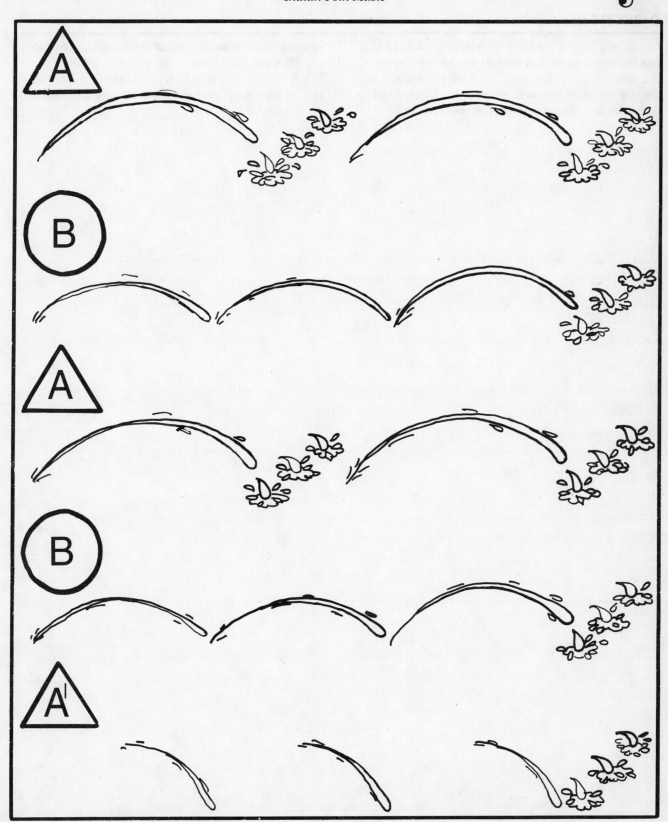

Macmillan/McGraw-Hill

USING RESOURCE MASTER C•7

DIRECTIONS:

Distribute a copy of the Resource Master to each child. Ask children how many A sections they see on the map (3), then how many B sections. (2) Each water stream on the map represents one sung phrase of music, often ending with three ascending strong notes, represented by splashes. Have children color all the A sections one color and the B sections another color to highlight the A B A B A' form. You may wish to have children move an arm, or move scarves or streamers, to show the shape of the melody for each phrase.

The Year-Naming Race, a folktale from China

Follow along as you listen to the story.

Many years ago in China, people waited each year for the seasons to return. Summer was hot, with long days. In the fall, the moon was big, and crops were ripe. Winter was cold, while warm breezes brought spring.

The people began to wonder how to tell one year from the next. Which was the year with no rain? How could they remember when their children were born? The people asked the Jade Emperor. He thought long and hard.

He called the animals to him. "I have decided to hold a race. All who wish to race will cross a wide river. The first twelve animals to reach the other side will have a year named after them."

Not all of the animals were good swimmers. They planned ways to cross the river. The cat and the rat were good friends. They asked the ox if they could ride on his back. The ox agreed.

The day of the race, the animals came to the river. There was a horse, a snake, a goat, a dragon, a monkey, a rabbit, a rooster, a tiger, a dog, a pig, the ox, the rat, and the cat.

Macmillan/McGraw-Hill

The rat and the cat climbed on the ox's back. The rat began to think, "The cat runs fast. She will win." Though the cat was his friend, he wanted to win. When the cat wasn't looking, he pushed her into the water! On shore, the rat ran to the Emperor. The ox was close behind.

The tiger got caught in the whirlpool. She used all her strength to reach the other side. The rabbit hopped from stone to stone. The dragon wanted to help some people who needed rain. He moved the rain clouds before he went to the Emperor.

The horse felt so sure he would win, he stopped to eat some grass. The snake slid by his feet, scaring him, and beating him to the Emperor.

The rooster found a raft. The monkey and goat helped him. All three crossed the river on the raft. The sheep went straight to the Emperor. The monkey did some funny tricks, and the rooster proudly walked behind.

The dog liked the river so much that he took a long time. The pig didn't like being so clean from the river. He stopped to roll in some mud.

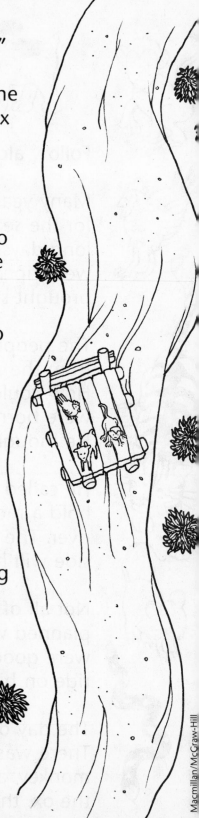

Macmillan/McGraw-Hill

Now all the animals had arrived. They lined up in front of the Emperor. He gave them medals.

"Rat, you work hard. You shall have the first calendar year."
"Ox, you are patient and alert, you shall have the second."
"Tiger, brave and strong, you have the third."
"Fourth is the rabbit—lucky and smart."
"Fifth is the dragon—soft-hearted and lively."
"Sixth is the snake—wise and calm."
"Seventh is the horse—sure and popular."
"Eighth is the goat—shy and gentle."
"Ninth is the monkey—funny and clever."
"Tenth is the rooster—smart and hardworking."
"Number eleven is the dog—loyal and honest."
"Finally, number twelve is the pig—strong and kind."
"I honor you," the Emperor said. "Now people will remember the important years."

Just then, the cat came in—wet and angry. "I'm sorry," said the Emperor. "There are already twelve winners."

The angry cat saw the rat and chased him. Since that day, cats chase rats, angry at the mean trick the rat played.

Macmillan/McGraw-Hill

RESOURCE MASTER LA•1

Concert Etiquette

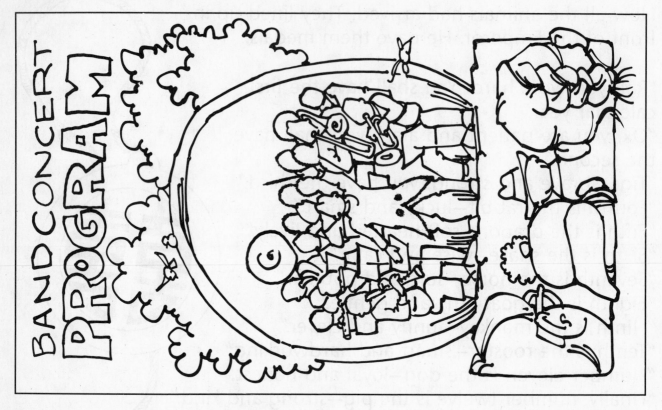

Mind Your Manners

1. Applaud when the conductor comes out. Applaud at the end of each piece when the conductor faces the audience.

2. Be a good listener. Do not talk while the band is playing.

3. If you attend an outdoor concert, leave the area clean when you go.

Macmillan/McGraw-Hill

Entry of the Gladiators
by Julius Fučik

As you listen, imagine the circus scene under the big top! You might see a circus parade!

Tattoo No. 1 in F
by Ludwig van Beethoven

Music that is used to call soldiers inside for the night is sometimes called a "tattoo."

March in place. If you hear a new section, change the way you are moving your arms.

The Stars and Stripes Forever
by John Philip Sousa

Listen to a famous march. Pretend you are playing one of the brass instruments. Which one did you choose?

Macmillan/McGraw-Hill

Name _____

Minuet and Trio (Third Movement)
from *Eine Kleine Nachtmusik*
by Wolfgang Amadeus Mozart

Listening Map concept by Diane Bethea Steele

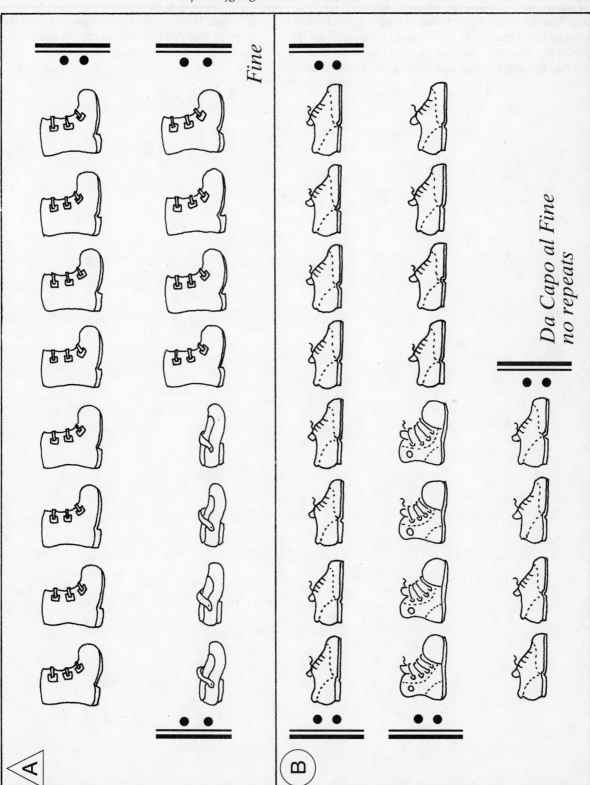

KEY | one shoe = one measure of $\frac{3}{4}$

Fine

Da Capo al Fine
no repeats

Macmillan/McGraw-Hill

USING RESOURCE MASTER LA·2

DIRECTIONS:

Distribute a copy of the Resource Master to each child. Ask children which shoes look similar. (first eight and last four of the A section, and first eight and last eight of the B section) Tell children that each shoe stands for three beats of music. Point out the repeat signs and the *Fine* and *Da Capo al Fine* (no repeats) indications and explain them to the children before listening.

Name _____

Waltz No.1
by Katharina Cibbini-Kozeluch

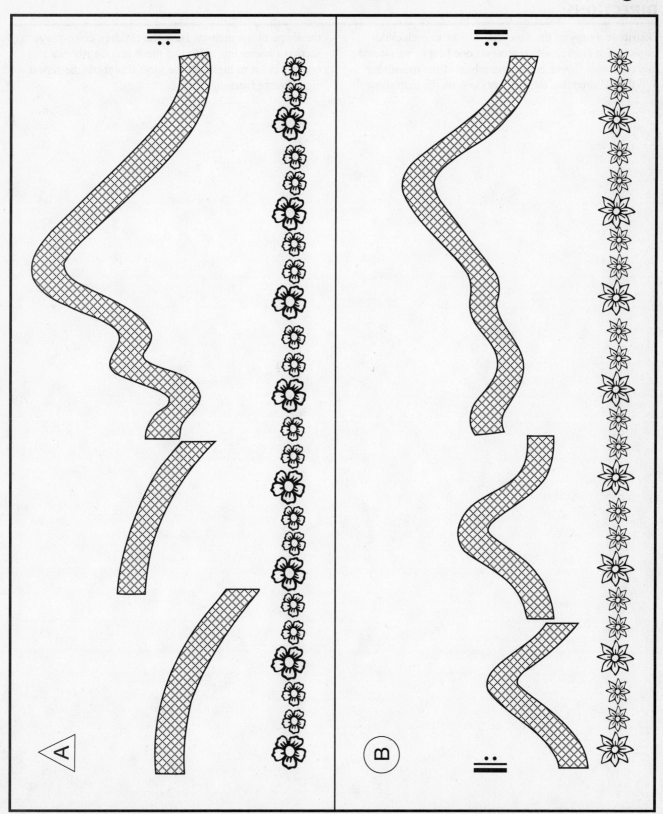

USING RESOURCE MASTER LA·3

DIRECTIONS:

Distribute a copy of the Resource Master to each child. Explain that each flower represents one beat of music and that the larger flower is the strong beat of the measure. Tell the children that the wavy ribbons on the map show the shape of the melody. Have the children color the A section ribbons one color and the B section ribbons another color to highlight the form. Point out the repeat signs before listening

Children's Chorus (excerpt) from *Carmen*

by Georges Bizet

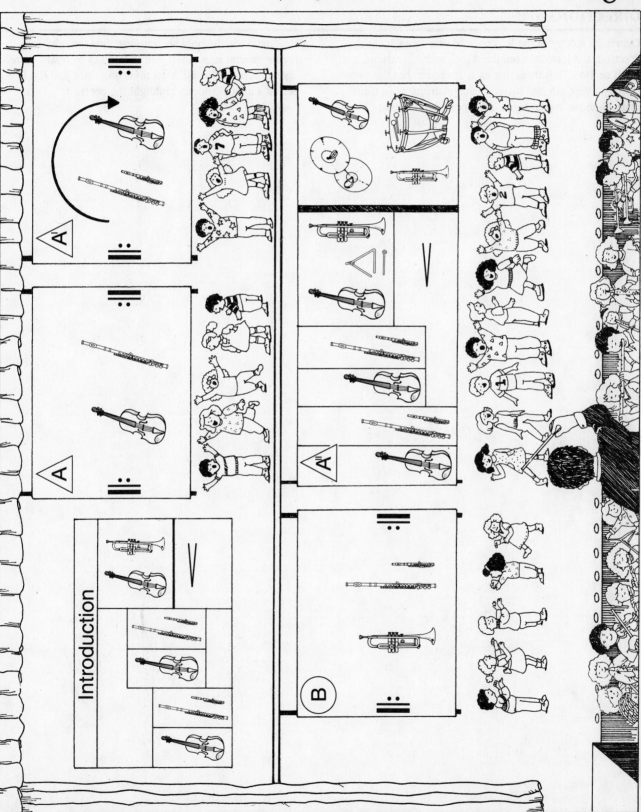

Listening Map concept by Debra Erck

Macmillan/McGraw-Hill

USING RESOURCE MASTER LA•4

DIRECTIONS:

Distribute a copy of the Resource Master to each child. Point out the Introduction, the A, A', and A" sections, and the B section. Tell them that each A section has the same melody. Point out and identify each instrument on the map. Note the repeat signs. Also point out that the introduction is the only section that shows no children singing around it, so their voices will not be heard there. Have children color all A sections one color and the B section another color to highlight the contrast.

The Aquarium from
The Carnival of the Animals
by Camille Saint-Saëns

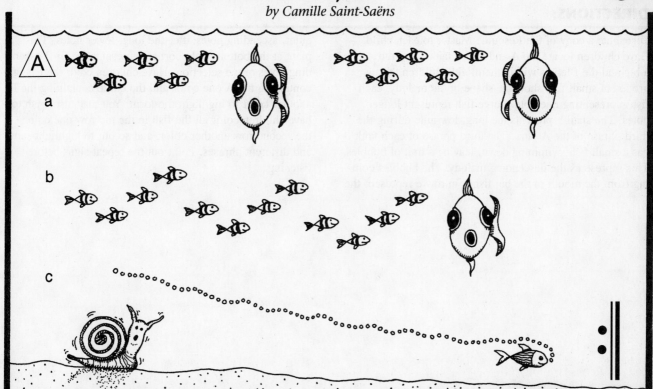

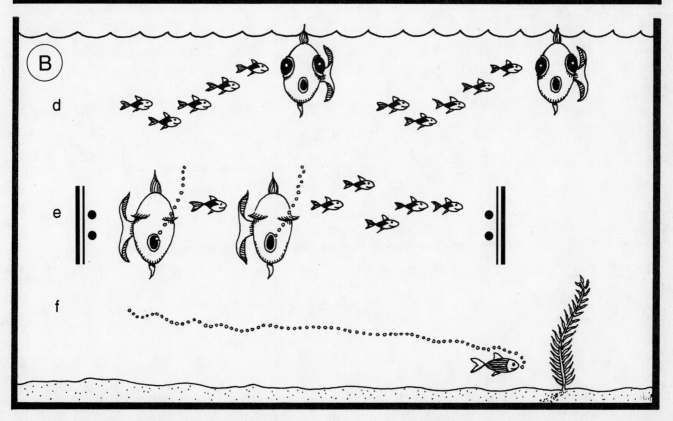

Macmillan/McGraw-Hill

DIRECTIONS:

Distribute a copy of the Resource Master to each child. Have children locate the A and B fish tanks, and the a b c and d e f labels within them. Tell children that groups of small fish show the shape of the melody, each fish representing one note. Large fish represent longer notes. The snail represents the long, low note during the third phrase of the A tank. The third phrase of each tank has a small fish swimming down, leaving a trail of bubbles. This represents the descending melody. The bubbles coming from the mouth of the big fishes in row e represent the quiet, ascending notes after the long, lower notes. The plant at the bottom right corner represents the final ascending notes of the selection. Have children color the triangle containing the A one color and the circle containing the B another color to highlight the form. You may also wish to have children color all the fish in the top row one color, the second row another color, and so on, to highlight same and different phrases. Point out the repeat signs before listening.

Children's Symphony, Third Movement
by Harl McDonald

Listening Map concept by Marilyn Buckner

Macmillan/McGraw-Hill

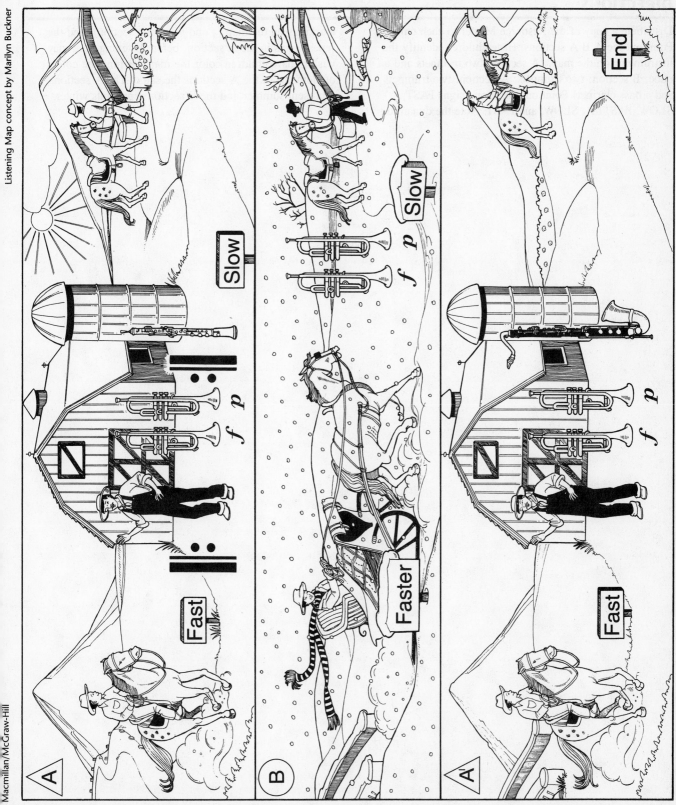

USING RESOURCE MASTER LA·6

DIRECTIONS:

Distribute a copy of the Resource Master to each child. Point out the A B A sections. Have children identify the instruments on the map. (A section: two trumpets and an oboe; B section: two trumpets; A' section: two trumpets and a bass clarinet) Point out the tempo signs FAST, SLOW, FASTER, SLOW, and FAST. Note the dynamic markings on the map (*f* and *p* in each section), and the repeat signs in the A section, before listening. You may wish to have children color the map, keeping the colors of elements of the A sections the same. The A sections represent summer and the B section represents winter.

Name _____

Seventy Six Trombones from Meredith Willson's *The Music Man*
by Meredith Willson

Introduction

 A — 76 110

 A — 76 110 reeds horns

 B

 B

Interlude

 A — 76

 A — 76  110 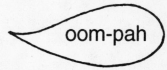 oom-pah

 A # ORCHESTRA

 A — 76 110 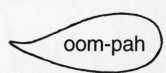 oom-pah

Listening Map concept by Sally K. Robberson

Macmillan/McGraw-Hill

USING RESOURCE MASTER LA·7

DIRECTIONS:

Distribute a copy of the Resource Master to each child. Have children find all the A sections (six), and the B sections. (two) Tell them that the pictures and numbers illustrate the words to the song. Have children find the two sections with no instruments or singers pictured. (interlude and penultimate section) Next, help children identify as many instruments pictured as possible:

Introduction: none

A: trombone, cornet

A: trombone, cornet, saxophone, clarinet, trumpet, French horn

B: timpani on horseback, double-bell euphonium, bassoon

B: (cannon) clarinet, bass clarinet, trumpet

Interlude: (no instruments)

A: trombone, gong

A: trombone, cornet, bass tuba

A: (no instruments)

A: trombone, cornet, bass tuba

Name _____

The Selfish Giant

From a Story by Oscar Wilde
Words and Music by John Horman

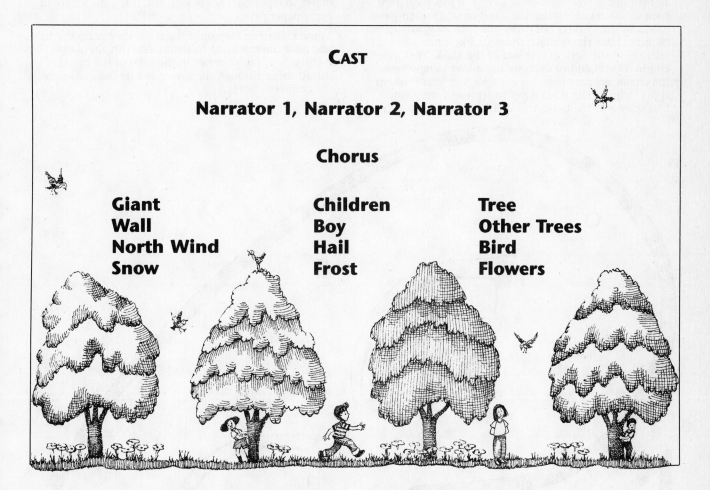

CAST

Narrator 1, Narrator 2, Narrator 3

Chorus

Giant	**Children**	**Tree**
Wall	**Boy**	**Other Trees**
North Wind	**Hail**	**Bird**
Snow	**Frost**	**Flowers**

(Play "Introductory Music." The curtain goes up on a beautiful garden. Trees, Flowers, Bird enter.)

Narrator 1: Once there was a giant. He had a big beautiful garden with green grass, flowers, and birds singing in the trees. Every afternoon after school, children played in the giant's garden. *(The children enter.)* And when the birds sang, the children sang, too.

SONG *(Children)*: "How Happy We Are Here"

Macmillan/McGraw-Hill

The Selfish Giant

To the teacher: Give each child a copy of this page. First have children cut out the mask and the strip, then paste masks to sturdy pieces of paper and trim away any excess backing. Have them attach the strip, like a handle, securely to the back of one side of the mask. Then have children color and/or decorate the masks to represent the characters they play. For example, the "giant" might apply strips of shredded paper to represent the wispy hair shown in the book, the "children" might color the masks to represent themselves, and the "flowers" could apply paper petals.

As the characters step onto the stage, they grasp the strips and hold the masks up to their faces. (An alternative method is to punch holes in the sides of the masks, thread string through the holes, and tie the masks onto the children's heads.)

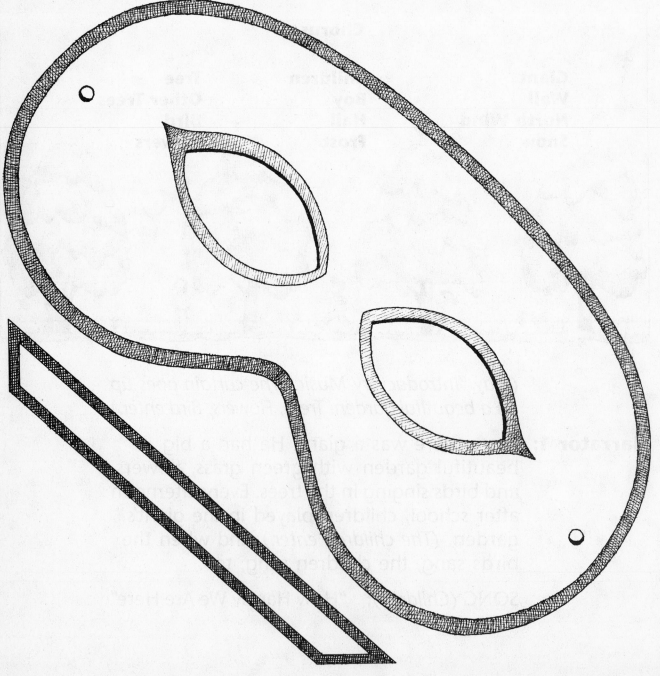

Macmillan/McGraw-Hill

Narrator 2: The children were able to play in the garden because the giant was away visiting a friend. At the end of the visit, the giant came back. (The giant enters.). When he saw the children in his garden, he yelled at the top of his voice.

Giant: Everyone out! Out of my garden! This garden is all mine. Only mine.

SONG (Giant): "What Are You Doing?"
(The children and the bird run offstage.)

Narrator 3: The frightened children ran away. Then the horrible giant built a high wall around the garden to keep the children out. (The Wall enters.) On the wall, he nailed up a sign that said—

TRESPASSERS WILL BE PROSECUTED
(The giant tapes the sign to the wall.)

Macmillan/McGraw-Hill

Narrator 1: He was a very selfish giant. Now the children had nowhere to play. (*The Children reenter.*)

Narrator 2: After school, they passed by the giant's wall and remembered the beautiful garden.

SONG (*Children*):
"How Happy We Were There"

Narrator 3: Something strange had happened beyond the wall. Spring never came. (*The trees drop their leaves.*) Summer never came. Fall gave golden fruit to every garden except the giant's. "He's too selfish," Fall said. (*North Wind and Hail enter.*) So it was always winter in the land. The North Wind and Hail danced through the trees. (*North Wind and Hail dance.*)

Macmillan/McGraw-Hill

North Wind and Hail: Spring, Summer, and Fall have forgotten this place. We live here all the time. Snow! Frost! Come dance with us.
(Snow and Frost enter and dance.)

CHORUS CHANT: "The Arrival of Winter"
SONG: "Spring Has Forgotten"

Giant: Brrrr! Where is Spring? Where is Spring? I do hope this weather will warm up soon.

(Snow, Frost, Hail, and the North Wind exit.)

Narrator 1: One morning when the giant was eating his breakfast, he heard a sweet sound.

(The bird enters.)

Giant: Look! A bird on my windowsill. I believe Spring has come at last.

SONG:
"Is That the Sweet Sound?"

(The trees pick up their leaves. Children enter and dance. One child stands away from the trees, shivering.)

Macmillan/McGraw-Hill

Narrator 2: The giant looked out his window again. The children had crawled into his garden through a hole in the wall. A child was sitting in every tree.

Narrator 3: The trees were so glad to have the children back again that they had covered themselves with blossoms. Birds sang and flowers smiled.

Narrator 1: In one corner of the garden, it was still winter. And in that corner a child stood shivering in the cold. He was too small to climb into a tree.

SONG *(Boy, Tree, Giant)*:
"The Song of the Boy, the Tree, and the Giant"

Macmillan/McGraw-Hill

Giant: How selfish I have been! Now I know why Spring never comes. I'll help that child into a tree. Then I'll knock down this horrible wall. *(The children run away. The shivering child stays.)*

Narrator 2: When the children saw the giant, they all ran away. Only the small boy stayed. He didn't see the giant because his eyes were full of tears. The giant took the child and gently lifted him into a tree. *(The giant and boy walk to one of the trees.)*

SONG *(Chorus)*:
"The Song of the Boy, the Tree, and the Giant"

Macmillan/McGraw-Hill

Narrator 3: The other children saw that the giant wasn't selfish anymore. So they came back, and with them came Spring. *(The trees pick up their leaves. The other children return.)* The giant kept his word and tore down that giant wall. *(The giant rips down the wall. The flowers return.)*

Giant: It's your garden now, children!

SONG *(Children)*:
"We're Back in the Garden Again"

Narrator 1: The years flew by, and the giant grew very old. *(The giant sits in a chair.)* He admired his garden and gazed at the children playing.

Giant: What wonderful trees. What wonderful flowers. But the children are the most wonderful of all.

SONG *(All)*:
"How Happy We Are Here" *(Reprise)*

Macmillan/McGraw-Hill

Name_____

The Tears of the Dragon

From a Story by Hirosuke Hamada, English version by Alvin Tresselt
Words and Music by Teruko Yaginuma
Script Translation from Japanese to English by Christopher Hanzie

CAST

Akito

Akito's Mother

Three Sparrows

Chorus

Village Children

The Dragon

The Tree

SCENE 1

(Stage back, rugged mountain. Stage right, ancient cypress tree. Stage center, village square with grass and flowers. Stage front, Akito fishes in a make-believe stream.)

(A child enters skipping. Then the child stands still and sings. More children enter and gather around him.)

SONG *(Children):* "Kakarenbo Game"

(At the end of the song, the children look at the mountain.)

SOUND EFFECT 1—Image Sound of the Dragon

(The children scatter in fright.)

SONG *(Children):* "I Am Afraid"

(The children exit. Akito stands near The Tree and the Three Sparrows. He turns to look at the mountain.)

Macmillan/McGraw-Hill

The Tears of the Dragon

To the teacher: Each child will need a large shoe box without the lid. Follow the steps below to guide children in creating a stage and characters for the play.

1. Explain that there are three "places" in the play:

   • the village green, with the cypress tree, green grass, and flowers against the towering mountains in the distance

   • the dangerous path up into the mountains where the dragon lives

   • the dragon's cave, cut into the mountains

2. Give each child a copy of the drawings on pages 114, 115, and 116 in this book of Resource Masters.

3. Explain that the oblong shapes show the places in the play and that the "people" in the ovals are characters in the play.

4. Have children color each of the oblong shapes. Then have them paste each colored shape on a sheet of heavy construction paper and trim off the excess paper along the long edges. Have them do the same with the characters and attach a strip of cardboard to the back of each character to make a puppet.

5. On the short sides of the box, have children cut two horizontal slots about an inch from the bottom. Children can slide the oblong strips through the slots to change the scenes.

6. Have children lay the box on one of its long sides at the edge of a desk or table. Have them use this "stage" and the puppet characters to perform the script.

Macmillan/McGraw-Hill

The Tree: A terrible, horrible dragon lives in that mountain.

Sparrow 1: Is he really so terrible?

The Tree: No one has ever seen him.

Sparrow 2: Oooooh! And he lives in that mountain?

Sparrow 3: No one has ever seen him?

The Tree: I can't say, myself, but people tell stories.

(Akito turns front and sings.)

SONG *(Akito)*: "Poor, Poor Dragon"

Mother: *(offstage):* Akito, it's getting dark! Come in now!

(Akito turns quickly and exits stage left.)

The Tree: Ummm, I think Akito is a very special boy.

All Sparrows: *(all together)* After all, nobody's ever seen the dragon. Maybe Akito's right.

SOUND EFFECT 2—End of scene

Macmillan/McGraw-Hill

SCENE II

(The Tree and the Sparrows remain as they were at the end of Scene I. Akito and his Mother enter, stage right.)

Mother: Akito, your birthday's coming up. Whom would you like to invite to your party?

Akito: Mother, I'm going to invite that dragon.

Mother: Oh, my!

Akito: I'll just go right out and meet him.

Mother: What? It will be a difficult journey all the way up that mountain.

Akito: I'll be O.K., Mother.

SONG *(Mother)*: "Akito, My Son"

SONG *(Akito)*: "Looking for the Dragon"

(Akito and his mother exit, stage left.)

SOUND EFFECT 2—End of scene

Macmillan/McGraw-Hill

SCENE III

Sparrow 1: The night is over . . .

Sparrow 2: And the morning has come . . .

Sparrow 3: And it's a beautiful day!

(The Sparrows flutter to The Tree. Akito and his Mother enter stage left.)

Akito: Mother, I'm going now!

Mother: Please be careful! *(Mother exits with a worried expression.)*

(Akito walks "up" a mountain path on the stage. Children's voices shout "It's scary! It's frightening! I'm afraid.")

SONG *(Children)*: "I Am Afraid"

The Tree: Akito's gone. All of you, quickly go after him, follow him, and watch out for him.

All Sparrows: We'll watch out for him from the sky.

INSTRUMENTAL: "Mountain Climbing"

(The stage darkens and Akito begins searching for the Dragon as he sings, accompanied by echoes from off-stage voices. The Sparrows follow.)

SONG *(Akito)*: "Hello, Dragon"

SOUND EFFECT 2—End of scene

Macmillan/McGraw-Hill

SCENE IV

INSTRUMENTAL: "The Mountain Song"

(Cave, stage center. The Dragon is unseen inside the cave. Note: The scene is set while song plays and repeats.)

Akito: Hello, Dragon! Where are you? Please come out.

SOUND EFFECT 1—Image Sound of the Dragon

(The Dragon's face appears in the cave. The Sparrows flutter in fright. Akito doesn't move.)

SOUND EFFECT 3—Appearance of Dragon

Dragon: Who's calling me?

Akito: Hello, Mr. Dragon. It's me, Akito. I've come to invite you to my birthday party.

Dragon: But I am big and frightening. No one has ever come to see me. Aren't you afraid?

Akito: Not one bit. So why don't we both go down to the village together?

Dragon: Really? Everyone will be afraid of me.

Macmillan/McGraw-Hill

Akito: I don't think so. I've met you, and I'm not afraid. Why should anyone else be?

(The Dragon's head is completely out of the cave.)

SONG *(Dragon):* "Thank You"

SOUND EFFECT 4—Tears of the Dragon

(The Dragon begins to cry loudly.)

Sparrow 1: Look, there are tears in the Dragon's eyes.

Sparrow 2: Oh, they're falling down his cheeks . . .

Sparrow 3: And making a river!

Dragon: O.K.! Everyone on my back and we'll be off to the village for Akito's birthday party.

FINALE

(The Dragon's body has become a boat on the river. The Sparrows and Akito have climbed on board.)

Akito: Let's go to the village!

SONG *(All):* "Let's Sing, Everyone"

(All characters on stage begin singing. Those offstage enter and join in the song.)

SOUND EFFECT 2—End of scene

Macmillan/McGraw-Hill

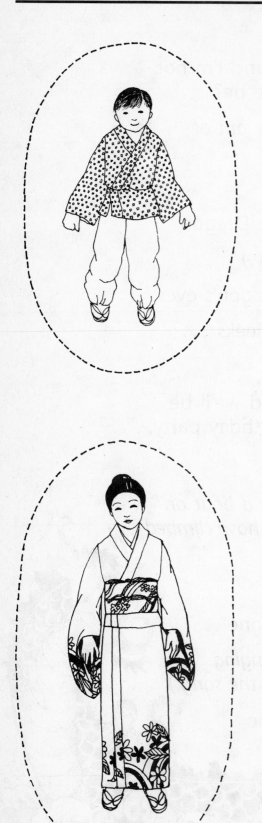

Macmillan/McGraw-Hill

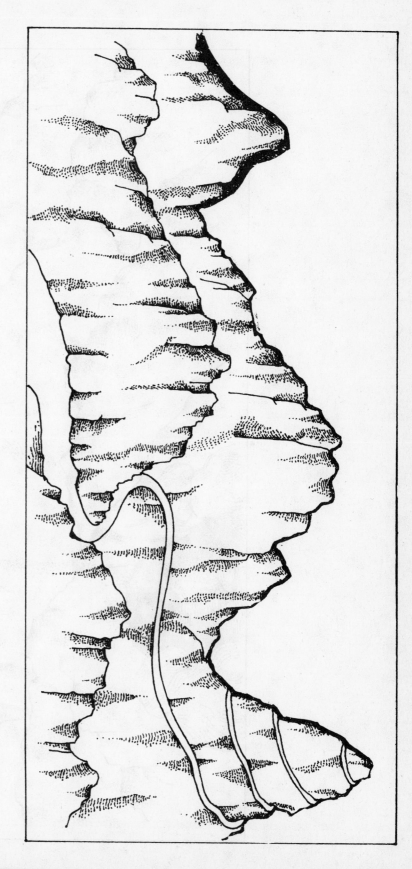

Macmillan/McGraw-Hill

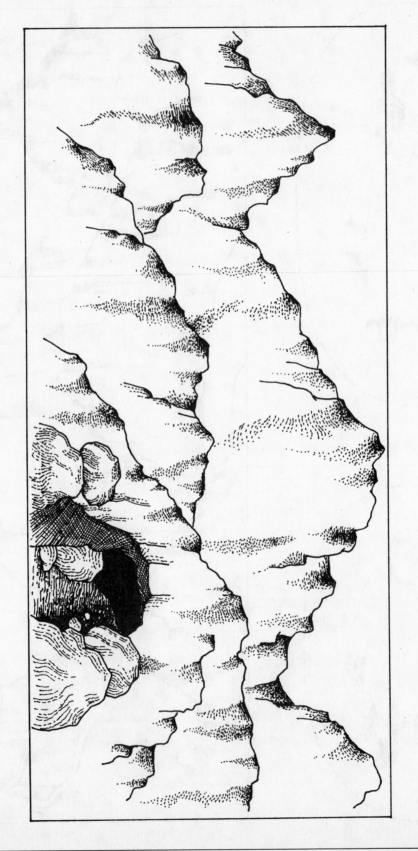

Macmillan/McGraw-Hill

Student _____ Date _____

Portfolio Evaluation Form

Directions: For each student, review the contents of the portfolio and assign a score of 1–4 for each criterion listed below. Determine a summary score for the entire portfolio, based on Criteria 1–12 (or more).

CONTENTS	Needs to Improve	Fair	Good	Excellent
1. **Completeness.** Meets all requirements.	1	2	3	4
2. **Variety.** Includes a variety of pieces.	1	2	3	4
3. **Organization.** Shows clear organizational plan.	1	2	3	4
4. **Volume.** Includes sufficient amount of work.	1	2	3	4
5. **Focus/Purpose.** Meets intended purposes.	1	2	3	4

ATTRIBUTES				
6. **Effort.** Demonstrates concerted effort.	1	2	3	4
7. **Quality.** Illustrates appropriate level of quality.	1	2	3	4
8. **Creativity.** Shows imagination and creative ideas.	1	2	3	4
9. **Risk-Taking.** Takes risks in creating/choosing works that go beyond minimum expectations.	1	2	3	4
10. **Growth.** Shows improvement.	1	2	3	4
11. **Reflection.** Shows signs of personal reflection.	1	2	3	4
12. **Self-Evaluation.** Shows awareness of strengths and weaknesses.	1	2	3	4

THINGS YOU'D LIKE TO ADD

13. _____	1	2	3	4
14. _____	1	2	3	4
15. _____	1	2	3	4

SUMMARY SCORE

Meets the requirements of program goals.	1	2	3	4

COMMENTS

Macmillan/McGraw-Hill

RESOURCE MASTER TA•2 Tools for Assessment

Student Assessment Cards

Directions: Help students complete one or more of these cards as an attachment for each item chosen for their portfolios.

Name of piece _____ Date _____

My description of this piece

Name of piece _____ Date _____

How I feel about this piece

Macmillan/McGraw-Hill

Interest Inventory

Put a check beside as many answers as you like.

1. I like to. . .

_____ listen to music   _____ move to music

_____ play music   _____ make up music

_____ sing songs   _____ perform for others

2. I'd like to know more about. . .

3. Here's an idea I'd like to try in music. . .

Name _____ Date _____

Self-Assessment Form

What I can do well	What I would like to do better
in listening	
in playing music	
in singing	
in moving to music	
in making up music	
in performing for others	

I'd like you to know. . .

Macmillan/McGraw-Hill

RESOURCE MASTER TA•5 Tools for Assessment

Music Log

Date	Title	What I Thought About It

Macmillan/McGraw-Hill

Answer Key

Resource Master 1•5, page 6

2. do — so mi la

Resource Master 1•7, page 8

TEST A

1. a   2. b   3. b   4. b

TEST B

1. b   2. a   3. c   4. c

Resource Master 2•4, page 13

2. so mi so ___

3. so mi mi so mi

4. so so do ___

Resource Master 2•8, page 17

TEST A

1. (fourth beat bar)   2. a   3. a   4. c

TEST B

1. (second beat bar)   2. b   3. c   4. a

Resource Master 3•1, page 30

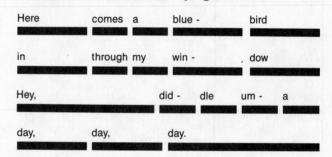

Here	comes a	blue-	bird
in	through my	win -	dow
Hey,		did - dle	um - a
day,	day,	day.	

Resource Master 3•7, page 36

Donkey, Donkey

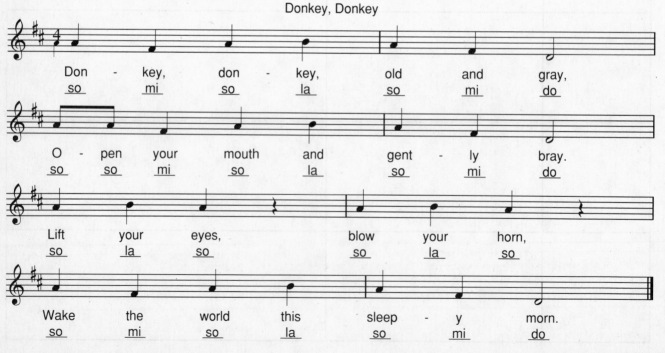

Don - key, don - key, old and gray,
so mi so la so mi do

O - pen your mouth and gent - ly bray.
so so mi so la so mi do

Lift your eyes, blow your horn,
so la so so la so

Wake the world this sleep - y morn.
so mi so la so mi do

Macmillan/McGraw-Hill

Resource Master 3•8, page 37

TEST A

1. c   **2.** a   **3.** b   **4.** c

TEST B

1. b   **2.** b   **3.** a   **4.** b

Resource Master 4•2, page 42

1.
so   so   so   so   la   so   so

so   so   so   so   la   so   so

so   so   so   so   la   so   mi   do

Lines 1 and 2 are the same.

Resource Master 4•3, page 43

The squirrel will jump on the set of three logs for *mi*; the set of two logs for *re*; and the single log for *do*.

Resource Master 4•5, page 45

1. do
do   re   mi   do   so   mi   so   do

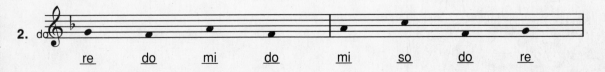

2. do
re   do   mi   do   mi   so   do   re

Macmillan/McGraw-Hill

Answer Key

Resource Master 4•7, page 48

do | do | do | re | mi | mi | mi

re | re | re | mi | do | do | do

do | do | do | re | mi | mi | mi

re | re | re | mi | do | do

Resource Master 4•9, page 50

TEST A

1. a 2. c 3. a 4. b

TEST B

1. c 2. a 3. b 4. c

Resource Master 5•3, page 56

Resource Master 5•4, page 57

TEST A

1. d

2.

3. b

4. a

TEST B

1. d

2.

3. a

4. b

Resource Master 6•1, page 59

1. d 2. b 3. a 4. c

Resource Master 6•2, page 61

Macmillan/McGraw-Hill

Resource Master 6•6, page 66

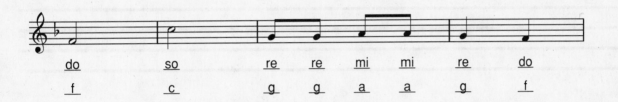

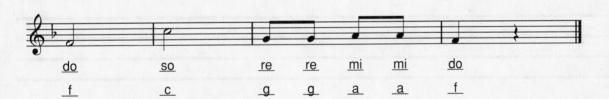

Resource Master 6•7, page 67

TEST A

1. c   **2.** a   **3.** b   **4.** c

TEST B

1. c   **2.** b   **3.** c   **4.** c

Macmillan/McGraw-Hill